Magical Herbs

Guide to Growing, Using, and Enjoying

DEDICATION

Contents

ACKNOWLEDGE

Did you know that much of modern medicine is derived from herbal medicine? In fact, many of the herbs that we grow in our gardens or right on the windowsill have healing properties.

And nothing beats cooking with home-grown herbs. Keep your kitchen supplied with fresh herbs all year with varieties that thrive on a sunny windowsill or under grow lights. For best results, give each herb its own pot so that you can customize care and give it room to grow.

So this book brings you advices on what herbs are the best to grow in the garden and how we should take care of your own herbs.

Are you ready? Let's go!!!

Things To Remember When Growing Herbs

An herb garden can be grown outside or inside depending on your needs, climate and space. There are advan   tages and disadvantages to both.

Indoor Advantages	Outdoor Advantages
Easy to access	Higher yields
No weeding	More flavorful
Year round growing season	More space

Whether you choose to grow inside or out, all herbs need plenty of sunlight, moderate temperatures, and a soil or potting mix that drains well. Keep in mind that most herbs are native to the Mediterranean

— provide them with conditions similar to this region and they will flourish. Of course, you can combine the two by growing in containers. This way herbs can be outside during the growing season and moved indoors when it gets cold.

5 Things You Need To Know

1. Herbs can be grown in any reasonably fertile, well-drained soil. Where drainage is questionable, create raised beds or plant your herbs in pots.

2. Good, all weather access is vital to growing herbs. If a hard path of light-coloured, reflective paving can be created, so much the better. At RHS Wisley, pebble/concrete panels are used in the herb garden, which reflect light back into the plants, and create warmth to ameliorate chilly nights.

3. Herbs generally need little fertiliser and crop well without much feeding. Over feeing can in fact decrease the concentration of flavours.

4. Most herbs need a neutral to alkaline soil.

5. High levels of sunlight is particularly important for obtaining good

herb flavour, and so herbs should be planted in the best lit area of the garden.

Indoor Gardens

Location is the most important choice you'll make in setting up an indoor herb garden. Herbs need at least 6 hours of bright sunlight, which may be tough to get during the winter months. To ensure plants are getting plenty of light consider the following:

Southwest facing windowsills offer the most light.

A corner with two windows (one facing south and the other west) is ideal.

Supplement with HID grow lights if your home doesn't get enough natural light.

Growing medium is a better choice than garden soil for your potted herbs. Choose an organic growing medium that is loose and drains well. You can purchase a commercial mix or make your own:

- *Soil Mix* – Use equal parts compost, sterile topsoil and builder's sand. An all-purpose organic fertilizer can be added to this mix.

- *Soilless Mix* – Combine 4-6 parts peat moss, 1 part perlite and 1 part vermiculite. If adding nutrients, blend 1/2 cup each bone meal, oyster shell lime (raises pH) and cottonseed meal/canola meal per 8 gallons of potting mix.

Water your plants enough to keep the soil moist without over-watering (roots will rot in a soggy container). Let the top of the soil, or growing medium, dry out completely between waterings and check moisture levels often. A moisture meter can help eliminate over and under watering by measuring moisture at the root level. It's also a good idea to plant herbs in separate containers, or make sure that plants grown together have similar watering needs.

Tip: Mint, parsley and lovage do best in fairly moist soil, whereas rosemary, thyme and sage prefer soil that is only slightly moist.

Seeds of annual herbs (basil, coriander, dill and oregano) can be started indoors and grown year round. Place a collection of popular culinary herbs in a sunny kitchen window and they'll be available when needed. Perennial herbs, like chives, parsley, sage, sweet marjoram and thyme, can be started from seed, but it is often easier to purchase young plants from a nursery. Because perennials grow for more than one season, it's best to keep them outside in pots during the summer and bring them in before the first frost.

Outdoor Gardens

Location is just as important for outdoor-grown herbs as indoor-grown. Figure out how much space each herb will need (read the seed packet or planting instructions) and how many plants you want to grow. Then calculate how much room you'll need for your garden. Also, choose a location that provides adequate amounts of sunshine.

Many herbs require 6-8 hours of sun each day to produce the essential oils that give them their pleasant taste and scent.

Soil will vary from area to area, but there are some specifics that all herbs need. Select a garden site with a well-drained loam soil, or improve the soil with the addition of aged animal manures, compost or peat moss. Quality soil should drain well, yet retain both moisture and nutrients. Also, use a soil test kit to test different areas in your garden. Soil pH affects nutrient availability to plants and can be adjusted by mixing oyster shell lime (raises pH) or elemental sulfur (lowers pH) into the soil. A slightly acidic to neutral soil (pH between 6.0-7.0) is best for the majority of herbs. If the soil in your area is really bad consider raised bed gardening. Filled with your own growing mix, a raised-box herb garden allows you to bypass poor soil altogether.

Prepare planting beds by digging 10-12 inches into the soil and turning it over. Get rid of any large stones. Then, mix in plenty of organic matter. Use a rake to level off the ground when you are done..

Water enough to keep the soil moist, but not soggy and avoid frequent light waterings which can draw roots to the soil surface. An occasional soaking is often better for plants. However, you do not want to wait so long between watering that herbs wilt or become stressed.

Tip: Group plants that have similar watering needs together and your herb garden will thrive.

Tips for You

Start Seeds Inside

If you know what you are doing starting seeds indoors can be pretty easy:

- Select containers. You can use seed trays or peat pots. You can also use egg cartons, yogurt containers or make your own pots from newspaper.
- Choose a high quality potting soil.
- Fill containers with potting soil and water. Don't let the soil get soppy, just evenly moist.
- Place the seeds on top and cover with a tiny bit of soil. Very small seeds can lie directly on the surface without being covered. Check your seed packet for specific planting guidelines.
- Place pots in a south-facing window where the temperature stays

between 60-75° F. A seedling heat mat can help keep your young plants warm.

- Read Ten Seeds Starting Tips to learn how a practiced propagator gets seedlings off to a healthy start.

Transplanting

After 5-10 weeks, your seedlings will be ready to move outside. But, don't just throw them out there and let them fend for themselves!

- Wait until the last danger of frost has passed and harden them off. To harden plants, leave them outside in the shade for progressively longer amounts of time each day. Start with a couple of hours and gradually work up to a full day and then overnight.
- Water plants an hour or two before transplanting.
- Transplant your herbs on an overcast day if possible, or in the evening to reduce shock.
- Prepare your beds before transplanting so that the move is quick.
- Loosen the herbs from the sides of their pots and gently rest them in a small hole in the ground. The plant's base should be even with the ground.
- Fill the rest of the hole and gently tamp down the ground.

- Water.

Direct Seeding

- Seed your herb garden after the danger of frost has passed.
- Read the seed packets to determine depth of planting.
- Prepare a trench to place the seeds at the correct depth. You can use your hands or a trowel for this.
- Scatter the seeds at the recommended spacing. It's better to plant too many seeds than too few — you can always thin the plants later.
- Cover seeds with a little soil. If you have a lot of clay in the garden, consider covering the seeds with vermiculite. Since clay absorbs heat from the sun, there is the possibility of your seeds getting burnt.
- Water gently.

Propagation by Division

By dividing existing plants, you can get new plants for free.

Divide plants in early spring before they start growing.

Use a spade to cut the roots. For smaller plants you may be able to pull the roots apart with your hands.

Add plenty of compost when re-planting your divided plant into it's new home.

Keep the soil moist – not sopping wet — until the new plant becomes established.

Chives, French tarragon and mint do well when propagated by division.

Maintenance

Once your herb garden is established you'll need to do a little maintenance to keep it flourishing (see Caring for Your Herb Garden). Herbs are generally pretty hardy, in fact many produce oils and chemicals that naturally repel pests. Some herbs, like sage and rosemary, seem to like harsh conditions that other plants eschew.

Occasionally, your plants may get attacked by insects, molds, mildews or other undesirables.

Mistakes New Herb Gardeners Make

Growing your own herbs can be very rewarding and enjoyable, but a few little things can make it frustrating as well. Learn ten mistakes new herb gardeners make and how you can fix them for ultimate garden success this year!

Mistake 1: Growing from seed.While there is something special about starting a plant from seed and watching it grow, there is a lot that can go wrong when starting seedlings. Seeds require a proper environment for germinating and being kept growing indoors before it's time to plant outside. For the same price (or less) as a packet of seeds, you can pick up your very own starter plants. This allows you to start with a healthy plant and avoiding the disappointment of not having plants to grow in the spring.

Mistake 2: Too complex, too early.When growing herbs, it's always best to grow what you love; after all you'll be eating them! At the same time, we're aiming for success when growing too. For a first time gardener, basil is a perfect trainer herb. It's a quick grower and it bounces back really well when not watered enough. This flexibility allows you to figure things out with a plant that can take a little abuse.

The fact basil is so versatile on recipes and a well-loved herb is yet another added benefit.

Mistake 3: You mean there's more than one kind of mint? *As in life, it's important to read carefully when choosing your herbs.* When you shop for groceries, there's no such thing as 'just an apple' there are many varieties available to you, same goes for selecting herbs. We've got plenty of thyme, no seriously, we actually have lots of different varieties of thyme; creeping thyme, silver thyme, lemon thyme, upright thyme, to name a few. When selecting herbs with multiple options available to you, know the flavour your looking to get and pick correctly. Otherwise you could want to make mojitos and grab apple mint instead of spearmint by mistake.

Mistake 4: Help, my soil isn't feeding me! A well-prepped garden with fresh soil can go along way. Using soil that is tired, with no nutrients left to offer you herbs isn't conducive to success. Spent soil that hasn't been worked, had compost added or been worked to turn up fresh soil doesn't give your herb a warm welcome to its new home. In your garden, turn over the soil and working in some digested compost is a more fitting home. In pots, avoid garden soil, yes you heard correct, avoid garden soils like topsoil or black earth! These soils are heavy and take forever to dry out after a rain. Using a potting soil or ProMix will be lighter and fluffier, perfect for herb growing. Add in an occasional watering (twice a month) with 20-20-20 water soluble fertilizer to recharge the nutrients your plants will take from the soil and you've made a bed fit for a (herb) king!

Mistake 5: Prevent a Garden Invasion! Some herbs provide complimenting flavours to our food but forget their manners when planted in your garden. Herbs like mint and oregano are voracious growers and get down right aggressive (even invasion) in a garden. To keep the rest of your garden plot safe, *consider growing these herbs in pots and burying them in the ground.* The added measure of control a pot puts on the roots of these herbs can keep them from moving in to the rest of your garden and prompting taking over. Of course the surest way to protect your garden from this threat is to grow them in pots grown above ground.

Mistake 6: Watering herbs like houseplants. There are a lot of differences between indoors and outdoors (duh) and those differences make growing plants outside very different than indoors. While herbs and house plants inside might do flourish with a good watering once a week, that just won't cut it for plants left in the garden. Most herbs will require moderate and regular watering's, especially in the hot summer months. If you're growing in pots, make sure the pot has adequate drainage; this will prevent your herbs from drowning after a long rainy period. The downside with growing in pots is your herbs will need even more water than if they're planted in the ground.

Mistake 7: Letting it all grow out. Knowing when to give your herbs a hair cut (so you can make a meal) can be difficult to judge but do it early and often. Just like the Medusa (or grey hairs), cutting one branch of a herb in the right place will lead to two more growing in it's place. It's a good practice to prune in V's (take a shoot just after two smaller ones) and the others will grow in larger. The cut stem won't grow any further, almost like a signal to your plant that it can grow that way. You can start trimming when your plant grows to 3-4" above the soil (making sure there are still some good leaves left behind), this will give you a sturdy base to grow on. As your herb grows back you can prune it every 3-4" of new growth, pruning back to with a couple inches of your last cut. After a few pruning's you so find your harvest yielding enough to fill out a recipe!

An added benefit to a good pruning, aside from increased yield, is a more compact and well-kept plant. Herbs that aren't pruned can grow tall and top heavy, a pruned herb is shorter and denser. Basil is a great plant to experiment with pruning but you'll find most plants (like annual flowers) will benefit from a good pruning too. Keep in mind, not all herbs are alike and some respond faster to pruning than others.

Mistake 8: Bigger isn't always best. When harvesting your herbs it's best to pick off the biggest leaves and leave the tender new ones, right? Wrong! It may seem counter productive but there are reason behind the madness of harvesting the new growth. First, those large older leaves are powering your herbs growth acting like big solar panels feeding the new growth up top. Removing lower leaves just leaves you with a tall skinny plant that won't support it's own growth. Second, remembering mistake 7 (let it all grow out), we want to take our harvest from leaves plucked up top and further proper pruning, the fact new leaves taste better is an added benefit. Don't forget to pluck above a V so new growth will replace the leaves you harvest.

Mistake 9: Flowers are not welcome at this party!Now, if you're following the advice about pruning and proper plucking, hopefully this mistake is not an issue you deal with. Flowers are pretty and lovely to see on our annuals or perennials, on herbs, they're normally a sign of nothing good. Unless yourgrowing something for its edible flowers, you should be cutting back herbs before they start growing flowers. Many people often note their sweet basil turns bitter in the middle of the summer and this is because those darn flowers ruin the flavour party. Add to that the fact herbs will focus all their energy on procreation and neglect growing if given half a chance, it's clear flowers (a plants reproductive parts) are to be avoided. Keep cutting off flower buds if you find them and it will keep your herb focused on growing leaves.

Mistake 10: Bring another herb (or 5) into your bed. So things have been going really well with that special herb or two and things seem to great, which is why it's time to spice things up and bring another herb (or five) into your bed. Variety is the spice of life and the more herbs you grow, the more flavour your food can have. For any foodie, this is a no brainer. Think of what you like to cook with and try adding it to your garden. Grown basil and had success? Why not try some rosemary, mint, oregano and thyme! We mentioned the many varieties available in herbs (mistake 3), so if you liked spearmint and had success with it, perhaps you can try growing chocolate mint. Add a pop of colour to your plate with purple leafed basil or a hint of citrus with lemon thyme. Just remember that like people, herbs respond differently to the care you give them. Most importantly, enjoy the experience of growing the herbs you'll use for cooking at home and have fun, success is sure to follow!

Step-by-Step to Grow Your Own Herbs

Growing Guide - Basil

Basil is a warm-weather, fragrant herb that tastes great in Italian dishes—and let's not forget homemade pesto! Plant seeds or transplants after all danger of frost has passed and soil is warm, and it will yield an abundant harvest within weeks. Keep harvesting the leaves to keep the plant going strong.

The most common type of basil is sweet basil; other types include purple basil (less sweet than common basil), lemon basil (lemon flavor), and Thai basil (licorice flavor).

Basil is easy to grow, but it only grows outdoors in the summer—and only once the soil has warmed up nicely—so plan accordingly.

If you're planning on making pesto, grow several plants. For other uses, one or two basil plants yields plenty.

PLANTING

WHEN TO PLANT BASIL

To get a jump on the season, start the seeds indoors 6 weeks before the last spring frost. (See local frost dates.)

To plant outside, wait until the soil has warmed to at least 50°F (10°C)—preferably around 70°F (21°C) for best growth. Nighttime temperatures shouldn't drop below 50°F (10°C).

Don't rush basil. Without heat, the plant won't grow well.

CHOOSING AND PREPARING A PLANTING SITE

Basil will grow best in a location that gets 6 to 8 hours of full sun daily, though it can perform well in partial sun, too.

Soil should be moist but well-drained.

Basil works great in containers or raised beds, as these allow for better drainage.

If you're planning on cooking with these plants, plant in clean soil, don't use insecticides, and grow them away from driveways and busy streets so that exhaust won't settle on the plants.

HOW TO PLANT BASIL

Plant seeds/seedlings about ¼-inch deep and 10 to 12 inches apart. They should grow to about 12 to 24 inches in height.

For larger varieties, plant farther apart (about 16 to 24 inches).

Tomatoes make great neighbors for basil plants in the garden—and on the plate!

HOW TO GROW BASIL

Make sure that the soil is moist. Basil plants like moisture.

If you live in a hot area, use mulch around the plants (the mulch will help hold in moisture and suppress weeds).

During the dry periods in summer, water the plants freely.

After the seedlings have produced their first six leaves, prune to above the second set. This encourages the plants to start branching, resulting in more leaves for harvest.

Every time a branch has six to eight leaves, repeat pruning the branches back to their first set of leaves.

After about 6 weeks, pinch off the center shoot to prevent early flowering. If flowers do grow, just cut them off.

If the weather is going to be cold or if a sudden frost is imminent, be sure to harvest your basil beforehand, as the cold temperatures will destroy your plants.

PESTS/DISEASES

Aphids

Powdery mildew

Variety of bacterial and fungal leaf, stem, and root diseases

HARVEST/STORAGE

HOW TO HARVEST BASIL

Start picking the leaves of basil as soon as the plants are 6 to 8 inches tall.

Once temperatures hit 80°F (27°C), basil will really start leafing out.

Harvest in the early morning, when leaves are at their juiciest.

Make sure to pick the leaves regularly to encourage growth throughout the summer.

Even if you don't need to leaves, pick them to keep the plant going. Store them for later use!

If you pick regularly, twelve basil plants can produce 4 to 6 cups of leaves per week.

HOW TO STORE BASIL

The best method for storing basil is freezing. Freezing will prevent the plant from losing a good portion of its flavor. To quick-freeze basil, package whole or chopped leaves in airtight, resealable plastic bags, then place in the freezer.

Another storage method is drying the basil (although some of the flavor will be lost). Pinch off the leaves at the stem and place them in a well-ventilated and shady area. After 3 to 4 days, if the plants are not completely dry, place them in the oven on the lowest heat setting with the door slightly open. Remember to turn the leaves (for equal drying) and check them frequently. See more about drying basil, tomatoes, and paprika.

RECOMMENDED VARIETIES

Cinnamon basil, to add a hint of cinnamon to a dish

Purple basil, to add some nice color to your garden (when steeped in white vinegar, it creates a beautiful color)

Thai basil, to add a sweet licorice flavor to a dish.

Growing Guide - Mint

Mint is a perennial with very fragrant, toothed leaves and tiny purple, pink, or white flowers. It has a fruity, aromatic taste.

There are many varieties of mint—all fragrant, whether shiny or fuzzy, smooth or crinkled, bright green or variegated. However, you can always tell a member of the mint family by its square stem. Rolling it between your fingers, you'll notice a pungent scent and think of candy, sweet teas, or maybe even mint juleps.

As well as kitchen companions, mints are used as garden accents, ground covers, air fresheners, and herbal medicines. They're as beautiful as they are functional, and they're foolproof to grow, thriving in sun and shade all over North America. In fact, mint can be vigorous spreaders, so be careful where you plant it.

PLANTING

Mints are vigorous perennials that thrive in light soil with good drainage.

Ideally, they prefer a moist but well-drained site, something like their native habitat along stream banks.

Most will tolerate some shade, and the variegated types may require some protection from direct sun.

For growing outdoors, plant one or two purchased plants (or one or two cuttings from a friend) about 2 feet apart in moist soil. One or two plants will easily cover the ground. Mint should grow to be 1 or 2 feet tall.

For the best growth in confined areas such as containers, topdress plants with a thin layer of compost or organic fertilizer every few months. Aboveground pots will need winter protection in cold climates.

In the garden, plant mint near cabbage and tomatoes—in pots, if possible, in order to prevent it from spreading and stealing nutrients from your crops!

How to Grow Mint

1. Take a cutting from a pre-existing mint plant. Mint is difficult to grow from seed, and it is virtually impossible for some varieties, like peppermint. Cut a 4 inch (10 cm) sprig about ½ inch (1 cm) above a junction to allow new branches to grow in its place. The sprig does not need to have many leaves, and almost any sprig will do. Place the sprig in a glass of water, and remove any leaves that fall below the water line.[1] Within a week, small white roots should appear under water. Wait a few more days to another week to allow the roots to develop into a decent length.

Add water to the glass as necessary. Make sure that you change the water every four to five days to prevent rot.

2. Purchase a mint seedling or small mint plant. You can find mint seedlings at most nurseries and garden stores. There are many varieties of mint, such as sweet mint, chocolate mint, spearmint, lemon mint, apple mint, and peppermint. Spearmint is most commonly used for cooking. Mint is a fast-growing, fast-spreading plant and is perfect for one of your first attempts at growing plants.

3. Find a runner from a current plant. Runners are long stems that grow away from the current plant and set their own roots in the ground. These can be carefully dug up and transplanted. If you have a friend growing mint, the plants will have runners that could be transplanted.

4. Choose the best time for planting the mint. Ideally, you should plant your mint in the spring, or in the fall if you're in a climate that is free of frost. Though mint is a resilient plant, it's best to start growing it under optimal conditions.

5. Transplant the seedling or rooted sprig into a container. Potting mint is the most popular way to grow it because you can easily keep it in check this way, as well as keeping it close to your kitchen so you can use it frequently. Mint spreads rapidly, and its roots have a tendency to choke out the roots of other plants. As a result, it is often best to plant mint in a container without other plants. Use a 12-to-16-inch wide pot for one plant.

You should add a water-retaining polymer to the potting soil so that it stays moist and doesn't dry up. You can also use pearlite or vermiculite instead of a polymer.

6. Plant the rooted sprig or seedling with the roots just below the soil. If planting multiple seedlings, plant them 6 inches (15 cm)

apart. This will give each seedling enough room to grow.

7. Choose a location with adequate sunlight. When you plant your mint or place down your potted mint plant, you'll need to choose an area that receives morning sun and partial afternoon shade. You want the plant to get some light without drying it out completely. Mint grows best in deep, moist soil, so you want to keep it that way. You can even place your mint pot indoors, on a windowsill, as long as it's in a location that will get enough sunlight.

8. Consider the location if you are planting in the ground. If you're planting it in the ground, then use a damp area with full sun or partial shade. The best conditions for growing mint in the ground require a fertile soil with a pH that is between 6.0 and 7.0. Though it can grow on its own without a problem, a little bit of fertilizer every few weeks won't hurt it. Make sure that the soil is moist by placing some mulch around the plant's roots to protect them.

9. Submerge the container if planting in a flower bed. If you go this route, you should submerge your mint in a container, such as a pot or a mesh bag that is at least 5 inches (about 13 cm) deep. You should leave the rim of the container above ground level so that the plant's root system will be contained. If you don't do this, your mint will spread rapidly into places you don't want it to be.

10. You can also plant mint in its own raised bed container, on a bare spot in your garden that you would like to fill in, or section off part of your garden with bricks or timbers to create a barrier for the mint.

CARE

Minimal care is needed for mint. For outdoor plants, use a light mulch. This will help keep the soil moist and keep the leaves clean.

For indoor plants, be sure to water them regularly to keep the soil evenly moist.

At first, mints develop into well-behaved–looking, bushy, upright clumps, but they soon set out to conquer new territory with horizontal runners and underground rhizomes. Unless you block the advance, a pert peppermint plant can turn into a sprawling 4-foot giant in just 1 year. It's not the stuff of horror movies, however. Mints benefit from picking and pruning. They are shallow-rooted and easy to pull out, so there's no reason to worry, as long as you provide physical barriers such as walls, walkways, or containers.

PESTS/DISEASES

Powdery mildew

Rust

Leaf spot

Anthracnose

Stem canker

Mice dislike the smell of peppermint. Spread it liberally where you suspect the critters. Mint is also considered a deer-resistant plant.

HARVEST/STORAGE

Frequent harvesting is the key to keeping mint plants at their best. Young leaves have more flavor than old ones, and mint can be harvested as soon as it comes up in spring. Although fresh is best and sprigs keep for a few days in water, mint leaves can be frozen or air-dried in bunches.

Right before flowering, cut the stems 1 inch from the ground. You can harvest one mint plant two or three times in one growing season.

You can also just pick the leaves as you need them.

You can grow the plants indoors for fresh leaves throughout the winter. If you want to dry them, it's best to cut the leaves right before flowering. Store the dried leaves in an airtight container.

PROPAGATING MINT

The best way to propagate mints is by taking cuttings from those that you like best. It's easy—take 6-inch cuttings of rooted stems and plant them horizontally in the soil. Mint stems will also root in a glass of water. Start with a small cutting from an established plant. Any gardening friend will give you a cutting of a favorite mint.

RECOMMENDED VARIETIES

Apple/Pineapple Mint: Mentha suaveolens

Corsican Mint: Mentha requienii

Pennyroyal: Mentha pulegium

Peppermint: Mentha x piperita

Citrus Mint: Mentha x piperita var. citrata

Spearmint: Mentha spicata

WIT & WISDOM

To relieve a tension headache, apply a compress of mint leaves to your forehead.

Mint is a symbol for virtue.

Mint can also help to relieve stress and anxiety.

Growing Guide - Oregano (Greek)

Oregano is a must-have in a culinary garden. Its pungent, spicy, slightly bitter flavor pairs well with almost any vegetable preparation. And just as easy to grow as chives, oregano is another go-to for the first-time gardener.

How to Plant Oregano

- Where: Oregano is one of those plants that looks beautiful planted within the landscaping or along a path. It is a "garden anchor" that comes back every spring, providing height and dimension within the garden. Oregano also grows well in containers, so if you live in a high-rise apartment or have a limited growing space, it is a great option. Oregano also performs well indoors, when given enough light and warmth.

- When: You can grow oregano by planting from seed, by dividing, or from a cutting taken from a healthy, established plant. When planting from seed, plant seeds outdoors about six weeks before the last frost. If you are planting a cutting or transplanting a seedling or small plant, make sure the ground temperature is at least 70°F.

How to Cultivate Oregano

Soil: Plant oregano in light, well-drained soil. Oregano actually grows better in moderately fertile soil, so no fertilization or addition of compost is necessary. I let my oregano do what it does on its own. My only complaint might be that I can't keep up with the harvest!

Sun: Oregano performs well in part to full sun, but the flavors intensify when it receives a full day of sunshine. Oregano will grow well indoors, but it is important that the plant receives adequate heat and sunshine in order to grow.

Water: Don't overwater oregano. Water thoroughly, only when the soil is dry to the touch.

Spacing: Plant oregano eight to 10 inches apart in your garden. Oregano grows up to two feet tall and spans about 18 inches across. If you are planting oregano in a container, be sure the pot is about 12 inches in diameter; oregano is a prolific grower. If you're limited on space, read this post on creating a small-space kitchen herb garden.

Companion planting: Oregano is a great companion plant to almost anything, so don't worry about planting it next to something it won't get along with. I plant oregano alongside my tomatoes and peppers. Oregano keeps away a tomato's archenemy, aphids, by means of predation. Aphids actually love oregano, but oregano also attracts *syrphidae* (flower flies), which then dine upon the small bugs. Oregano's thick foliage also provides humidity, which supports peppers' growth.

How to Harvest Oregano

Harvesting oregano couldn't be simpler. You may harvest oregano once the stems are at least four inches tall. I tend to let mine grow to about eight inches tall, and then I cut back up to 2/3 of the plant. Reference the photo above and cut just above the leaves. And don't worry if you think you've cut back your oregano too much — regular trimming encourages new growth and prevents "legginess."

→ **Tip: Want to know the** *easiest* **way to harvest oregano?** If you won't be drying your oregano by the bunch, and you only need the leaves, simply grab the stem about 2/3 down the length of the plant and run your fingers along the stem. The leaves will collect in your hand, and then all you'll have to do afterwards is trim the now-leafless stem. *Eureka!*

To obtain the optimum potency of flavor, harvest oregano leaves just before the plant flowers, if you can time it perfectly. Even the subtly flavored flowers are great topped on salads. Otherwise, either clip as needed or, as I do, trim your oregano plants all at once and turn on the dehydrator. More on what to do with your oregano when we discuss the best way to preserve your harvest in tomorrow's post.

Growing Guide - Rosemary

Rosemary (Rosmarinus officinalis) is relatively easy to grow, making it a good choice for any home herb garden. Its pungent flavor and pinelike scent make rosemary a popular ingredient in foods. The upright varieties are best for both fresh and dried use.

Rosemary can be grown as an annual (completes its life cycle in 1 year) or a perennial (completes its life cycle in 3 or more years). In herb gardens, it is often planted along with thyme, oregano, sage, and lavender. When planting, choose a variety that is suitable to the climate, soil, and desired use.

Soil preparation

Follow these steps to prepare the soil:

Remove all rocks, shrubs, weeds plant debris, and tree roots from the area to be planted.

Collect a soil sample and have it analyzed to determine your soil's fertility level. For information about the Texas A&M Soil, Water and Forage Testing Laboratory, visit http://soiltesting. tamu.edu/. 3. If needed, fertilize according to the soil test results to supplement the nutrition added from compost or organic matter. If the pH is too low, add lime to make the soil more alkaline.

Add about 4 inches of organic matter or compost to the surface and incorporate it with a pitch fork or a rototiller to a depth of 6 to 8 inches. Raised or slightly mounded beds provide the best drainage for the herb.

Planting

Like most herbs, rosemary is fairly drought resistant and, if healthy enough, can tolerate a light freeze. It is most successful when grown from cuttings or transplants. Although seed is readily available and usually inexpensive, its germination rate is usually only about 15 percent.

The best way to propagate rosemary is by taking a cutting from an already vigorous plant:

Clip a 3-inch branch from the stem of the plant.

Trim off most of the lower leaves to 1½ inches up the stem.

Plant one or two cuttings into a 3-inch pot.

Water the cuttings.

Place the pot in a windowsill with indirect sunlight and temperatures between 60° and 70°F.

After about 8 weeks, the cuttings will be rooted and ready for transplanting to their permanent location.

Fertilizing

Rosemary seldom needs fertilizer. But if growth is slow or the plant appears stunted or pale yellow, apply fertilizer once in early spring before new growth appears. Any allpurpose fertilizer in dry or liquid form is suitable as long as it is applied correctly. To prevent leaf burning, avoid applying fertilizer directly onto the plant.

Watering

Too much water can cause root rot. Sometimes it can be difficult to determine when a rosemary plant needs water because its needles do not wilt as broad leaves do. On average, water rosemary every 1 to 2 weeks, depending on the plant size and climate conditions. Allow the plants to dry out thoroughly between each watering.

Diseases

Although rosemary resists most diseases, some cases of powdery mildew have been reported. To prevent the disease from spreading, check the plants regularly and apply the proper fungicides when needed.

You can reduce the incidence of diseases by pruning overgrown plants to improve air circulation within the plants. Pruning also stimulates them to produce new shoots.

Insects

Rosemary is fairly resistant to pests. If spider mites, mealy bugs, or scales do appear, any organic or inorganic insecticide may be used.

If the plant has scales, an easy solution is to clip off and discard the infested plant tips; scales are sedentary insects. For mealy bugs, spray the plants with water, pyrethrum soap, or a soap-based insecticide.

Insects that suck plant sap are generally more prevalent in areas where too much nitrogen fertilizer has been applied. You can avoid most insect problems by fertilizing properly.

Harvesting

Once the plant grows to a suitable size, you can pick several small branches without harming it. Nursery plants can be harvested sooner than cuttings or seeds

Source	Length of time
Nursery plant	3 months
Cuttings	1 year
Seed	15 months

Rosemary plants can be harvested several times in a season, but they should be allowed to replace their growth between harvests. Some varieties are valued for their small flowers, which are harvested for use in salads.

The clippings can be used fresh or dried for later use (Fig. 2). Fresh cuttings will retain their best flavor for 2 to 7 days in the refrigerator. To store rosemary for longer periods, hang it in bundles to dry.

Growing Guide - Sage

Garden sage is easy to grow—and a wonderful culinary herb that flavors meat and bean dishes (including that Thanksgiving stuffing). See how to plant, grow, and harvest sage.

Sage is a hardy perennial with pretty, grayish green leaves that like as good in a perennial border as they do in a vegetable garden. It grows spikes of spring flowers in different colors, including purple, blue, white, and pink.

HOW TO PLANT SAGE

Plant sage in full sun.

Sage should be planted in well-draining soil; it won't tolerate sitting in wet soil.

The easiest and best way to start sage is from a small plant. Set the plants 2 feet apart.

You can also sow seeds up to two weeks before the last frost date. (See local frost dates.) Plant the seeds/cuttings in well-drained soil 1 to 2 weeks before the last spring frost.

For best growth, the soil should be between 60° and 70°F.

Plants should grow to be between 12 and 30 inches in height.

In the garden, plant near rosemary, cabbage, and carrots, but keep sage away from cucumbers.

CARE

HOW TO GROW SAGE

Be sure to water the young plants regularly until they are fully grown so that they don't dry out. They'll need a consistent moisture supply until they start growing quickly.

Prune the heavier, woody stems every spring.

It's best to replace the plants every few years so they remain productive.

PESTS/DISEASES

- Rust
- Powdery mildew
- Stem rot
- Fungal leaf spots
- Whiteflies
- Aphids
- Spider mites

HARVEST/STORAGE

HOW TO HARVEST SAGE

Pinch off leaves or snip off small sprigs from the plant.

During the first year, harvest lightly to ensure that the plant grows fully.

After the first year, be sure to leave a few stalks so that the plant can rejuvenate in the future.

If fully established, one plant can be harvested up to three times in one season.

Stop harvesting in the fall so the plant can prepare for winter.

HOW TO STORE SAGE

Sage's flavor is best when fresh, but it can be stored frozen or dried.

To dry, hang sprigs in a shady, well-ventilated area and allow them to air dry, waiting until the leaves crumble easily to store in tightly lidded jars.

Sage keeps its flavor better if stored in the freezer. Freeze leaves or stalks on a tray, then move the leaves into a zippered bag or container. Some cooks blend the leaves with oil, pack the ground mixture into ice cube trays to freeze, and then transfer the cubes to a container.

RECOMMENDED VARIETIES

'Tricolor' sage, for a bit of color in the garden (yellow, mauve, and sage green)

Growing Guide - Chives

Chives are a low maintenance, easy to grow perennial herb, grown for their onion-scented tasting leaves. These are a delicious addition to salads, and can be added to many other savoury dishes.

Their taste is milder than onions, so they are the perfect choice for soups and savoury dishes – where their more subtle flavour is needed. Although mainly grown for their leaves, chives also produce highly attractive pinky-purple flowers. These are also edible and are an attractive salad garnish. They also attract bees and butterflies,

How to grow chives

Cultivation

Chives will grow perfectly well in a position in full sun or in partial shade. They grow best in a fertile, moist but well-drained soil. Dig in plenty of organic matter – such as garden compost, well-rotted manure or other soil improver – especially in very well-drained sandy soils to hold moisture. Add grit or sharp sand to heavy clay soils to improve drainage if needed.

Chives varieties

The usual chives grown as a herb, is the straight species, *Allium schoenoprasum*. You may also find Staroand Fine Leaved, which have a milder flavour, and Forescate, with a slight garlic flavour and pale pink flowers.

Sowing chives

You can sow chives seeds thinly outdoors in spring where you want them to grow. Prepare the soil well with added compost or other soil improver and rake to a fine tilth before sowing. Thin out the young plants to 23-30cm (9-12in) apart when large enough to handle.

Seeds can also be sown indoors from March to June in pots or cell or plug trays filled with seed sowing compost at a temperature of 18-21C (65-70F). Lightly cover the seed with more compost and keep moist. When seedlings are large enough to handle, transplant into

7.5-10cm (3-4in) pots in bunches of 4-6 seedlings per pot. Grow on the seedlings in cooler conditions of around 10C (50F) and plant outside when the last frosts are over, after hardening off – gradually acclimatising them to outdoor conditions – for 10-14 days.

Planting chives

You can buy young parsley plants from garden centres, which can be planted outside any time of year.

Dig over the planting area, incorporating some organic matter – such as compost or leafmould if the soil is heavy clay. Dig a good sized hole big enough to easily accommodate the rootball.

Place the rootball in the planting hole and adjust the planting depth so that the crown of leaves is at soil level.

Mix in more organic matter with the excavated soil and fill in the planting hole. Apply a general granular plant food over the soil around the plants and water in well.

Or grow them indoors on a brightly lit windowsill to have fresh leaves readily to hand.

How to care for chives

Chives are very easy to look after and need minimal maintenance.

Keep the soil moist by watering regularly during prolonged dry periods in summer.

Feed with a general granular plant food each spring.

Plants may become congested over time and need rejuvenating every 3 to 5 years. Carefully lift, divide the plant into smaller portions and replant in well-prepared soil in spring.

To keep the plants productive and with the best-flavoured leaves, remove flowers as they form or cut them when young for brightening up salads.

When chives die back in late autumn, clear away all dead leaves and any other debris.

Harvesting

Harvest leaves as needed with scissors, cutting them back close to the base of the plant. The more regularly they're cut, the more new leaves they will produce.

Chives are best used fresh, as soon as they are cut. They can be frozen by cutting them up and packing into ice cube trays with water.

Magical Herbs

Flowering season(s)	Summer
Foliage season(s)	Spring, Summer, Autumn
Sunlight	Partial shade, Full sun
Soil type	Chalky, Clay, Loamy, Sandy
Soil pH	Neutral
Soil moisture	Moist but well-drained
Ultimate height	40cm (16in)
Ultimate spread	30cm (12in)
Time to ultimate height	6-9 months

Growing Guide – Cilantro/Coriander

How to Grow Cilantro

Cilantro **needs full sun or light shade** in southern zones since it bolts quickly in hot weather. It grows best in a well-drained, moist soil. Cilantro plants should be spaced about **6 to 8 inches apart**. To harvest fresh cilantro all season, make successive **sowings every 2 to 3** weeks starting in late spring.

From the time of sowing seed, cilantro leaves can begin to be harvested in about 3 to 4 weeks. Cilantro seeds can be harvested in about 45 days.

Cultivating Cilantro Seeds and Plants

Prepare soil by adding some compost or other organic matter to the planting area and working it into the soil to a **depth of at least 18 inches**. Rake the area smooth. Sow cilantro seeds 1/4-inch deep directly in the garden in late spring or early summer. Sow seeds or thin to 6 to 8 inches apart in rows spaced about 1 foot apart. Provide plenty of moisture and feed cilantro plants with a water-soluble fertilizer when they reach about 2 inches in height.

Since cilantro grows so quickly, it can also be sown again in the fall in warmer zones. For a steady supply of fresh leaves all summer, make successive sowings of cilantro seed every 2 to 3 weeks beginning in the spring.

Cilantro Growing Tips

When growing cilantro, the aim is to maximize foliage. Pinch back young cilantro plants an inch or so to encourage fuller, bushier plants. Snip off the top part of the main stem as soon as it appears to be developing flower buds or seedpods. Cutting off the flower heads redirects the cilantro plants' energy back into leaf, and not flower or seed production.

Watch the plants carefully as the weather gets hotter. Cilantro has a short life cycle and bolts quickly (develops seed) in hot weather. Once cilantro sets seeds, the plant quickly starts to degrade.

If seeds are allowed to develop, you'll notice how easily cilantro self-sows when you see delicate, lacy-leaf seedlings growing up around mature plants.

What Insects & Diseases Affect Cilantro?

Cilantro rarely has serious problems with insects or diseases. In fact, probably **due to cilantro's strong scent, it is considered an insect repellant**. Two diseases that could be a problem are **leaf spot and powdery mildew**. Leaf spot appears as small yellow spots that turn into larger brown spots. Excess moisture and poor air circulation most often cause the problem. Prevent leaf spot by making sure cilantro plants are grown in a well-drained soil, are not over watered, and are thinned out enough to allow good air circulation around them.

Powdery mildew appears as a powdery white coating on the foliage usually during hot, dry periods. Prevent powdery mildew by giving cilantro plants adequate moisture and avoid overcrowding.

Cilantro Harvesting Tips

For Cilantro

The leaves can be cut at any time. Use the upper, new, finely cut leaves in cooking, but not the mature, lower ferny-type leaves. Cilantro is not normally saved and dried like other culinary herbs since, as stated, it loses almost its entire flavor when dried.

For Coriander

The large coriander seeds are easy to harvest and handle. Harvest on a dry day. Cut the top of the stems when the seedpods begin to turn brown and crack if pressed. Make sure pods are harvested before they release seeds into the garden. Once stems are cut, place seedpods in a paper bag so seeds will be caught. Finish the ripening process for a few weeks in a dark, well-ventilated, cool place. Pods can be shaken or rolled around in your hands to release the seeds.

Printed in Great Britain
by Amazon

43356636R00037